To Mike & Barbara Rowarth of Haydon
With thanks for friendship, support
over many years of ministry

SIMEON

A Christmas Musical by

Roger Jones

With other words by Martin Parry & P Brooks
Narrative links by Beresford King-Smith

24 Spadesbourne Road
Lickey End
Bromsgrove
B60 1JP
0845 307 6279
Email: office@cmm.org.uk
Website: www.cmm.org.uk

First printed 1997
Reprinted 2011

ISBN 1 874594 41 4

Cover design by **Andrew Jones**

Music Score edited by **Ann Routley**

(during intro. To Verse 1 of opening song)
SIMEON *My name is Simeon. How does the Psalmist put it? "I have been young, and now am old ..." We are in the Temple courts – a busy place, with lots of buying and selling. But I come here every day, to pray and feel close to my heavenly Father.*

(during Verse 2)
Many years ago, God filled me with His Holy Spirit and promised that before I die I shall see the Messiah – the Anointed one – with my own eyes. And here are Mary and Joseph, bringing their baby son Jesus into the Temple. As I take this small boy into my arms I know that He is indeed the promised Messiah!

(1) O COME, O COME EMMANUEL

- Nunc Dimittis (= "Now dismiss")

Roger Jones

Gently ♩ = 70

Dm C Dm Gm9 Am7Dm

(SIM - Narration starts before music)

Dm C Dm Gm9 Am7Dm

(SIM) "We are in the Temple courts ...."

(TB) O

2nd - (SIM) "Many years ago ...."

Dm Gm C F *1st only* Gm Asus4

1st - sung
2nd - oohs

(SA) Nunc di-mit- tis

come, O come, Em-ma- nu- el, and ran-som cap-tive Is- ra-

Dm
Gm
F
G
C
Nunc di-mit- tis
Nunc di-mit- tis
el, that mourns in lone- ly ex- ile here, un-
Am
Gm
C
F
C
Am
Nunc di-mit- tis
til the Son of God ap- pear. Re- joice! Re- joice! Em-
Gm
C
F
B♭
Gm7
Asus4
1
Dm
shall come to thee, O Is- ra- el.
ma- nu- el shall come to thee, O Is- ra- el.

2
faster
♩ = 80
Dm
C
(SA) Nunc di- mit- tis
el.
(TB) Nunc di- mit- tis
Dm
Gm9 Am7 Dm
Dm
Nunc di- mit- tis
Lord we pray!
Nunc di- mit- tis
Lord we pray!
C
Dm
Gm9 Am7 Dm
Nunc di- mit- tis
Lord we pray!
Nunc di- mit- tis
Lord we pray!

(SIM)
Dm
C
B♭
Am7
(choir)
Lord, now let your ser- vant de- part in peace, ac- cor- ding
Gm7
Am7
Dm
C/D
(SIM)
Dm
C
to your word.
Lord, now let your ser- vant de-
B♭
Am7
(choir)
Gm7
Am7
Dm
part in peace, ac- cor- ding to your word.

SIMEON *Mary and Joseph told me their story. They come from Nazareth, and some months ago, when Mary was already engaged to be married to Joseph, an amazing thing happened. A messenger of God named Gabriel appeared and greeted her. He told her that she had found favour with God and was to give birth to a very special boy-child, fathered not by Joseph but by the Holy Spirit.*

(2) WHY SHOULD I BE SO FAVOURED?

Magnificat

Roger Jones

B♭
E♭/Bb
Fsus4
Cm/F
F7
I will
mag- ni- fy
the
Lord!
B♭
E♭/Bb
Fsus4
Cm/F
F7
I will
mag- ni- fy
the
Lord!
Oh -
B♭
E♭/Bb
Fsus4
I will
mag- ni- fy
the
Lord!

D9/F#
Gm7
Praise His name, pro- claim His word,
Cm/Eb
E♭sus2
B♭
B♭sus4
B♭
B♭sus4
He is my God!
(MARY)
F
E♭/Bb
B♭
F
E♭/Bb
B♭
All gen- er- a- tions will now call me bles- sed,

(choir)
E♭
E♭/F
F7
E♭/Bb
B♭
E♭/Bb
B♭
He has been mind- ful of my hum- ble state.
(MARY)
F
E♭/Bb
B♭
F
B♭
(choir)
See how the migh- ty One has done great things for me, and
G♭
A♭7
B♭
ho- ly is His name!

B♭
E♭/Bb
(MARY)
Fsus4
Cm/F
F7
I will mag-ni- fy the Lord!
I will mag-ni- fy the Lord!
B♭
E♭/Bb
Fsus4
Cm/F
F7
I will mag-ni- fy the Lord!
I will mag-ni- fy the Lord!
Oh -
B♭
E♭/Bb
Fsus4
I will
I will mag- ni- fy the Lord!

D9/F#
Gm7
magnify the Lord!
Praise His name, proclaim His word,
Cm/Eb
E♭sus2
B♭
B♭sus4
B♭
D9/F#
He is my God!
Praise His name,
Gm7
Cm/Eb
E♭sus2
B♭
B♭sus4
He is my God!
proclaim His word,
He is my God!

B♭
D9/F#
Gm7
He
Praise
His
name,
pro-
claim
His
word,
Cm/Eb
E♭sus2
B♭
B♭sus4
B♭
B♭sus4
is
my
God!
He
is
my
God!
G♭
A♭
B♭
Mag-
ni-
fy
the
Lord!
Mag-
ni-
fy
the
Lord!

SIMEON *One day a proclamation was read out in the market place in Nazareth. The Roman authorities were taking a Census. Every householder would have to return to the town from which his family had come in order to register.*

(3) CAESAR'S FRACTIOUS

Martin Parry

Roger Jones

Fm6/D
(JOS)
Cm
Fm6/C
Gsus4/C
G/C
They will count us in a cen- sus, one by one each man and wife!
Ah-
Fm6/C
(MARY)
Cm
Fm6/C
Gsus4/C
G/C
Such a fuss and such a bo- ther, such an up and down in life!
D♭m7
(M & J)
Gsus4/G
G
Cm
Fuss and bo- ther! Such an up and down in life!
Such an up and down in life!

Dm C Dm Am7 Dm C Dm Am7 Dm
Dm (JOS) C Dm C
From His- pa- nia to Ju- de- a
(choir) Mo- ney, mo- ney, mo- ney, mo- ney!
Dm (MARY) C Dm Am7 Dm
Cae- sar rules from there to here -
Mo- ney, mo- ney! He wants more!

Gm6/D
(JOS)
Dm
Gm6/D
Asus4/D
A/D
Ro- mans want to rule the roost, so ev'- ry- one must run and do!
Ah-
Gm6/D
(MARY)
Dm
Gm6/D
Asus4/D
A/D
What the Rom- ans want I ask you, Oh but if they on- ly knew!
E♭m7
(M & J)
Asus4/D
A/D
Dm
What I ask you! Oh but if they on- ly knew!
Oh but if they on- ly knew!

Em D Em D Em D Em Bm7 Em
Em (JOS) D Em D
What's the sense of cen- sus ta- king
(choir) Mo- ney, mo- ney, mo- ney, mo- ney!
Em (MARY) D Em Bm7 Em
Just a lot of trou- ble- ma- king
Mo- ney, mo- ney! He wants more!

Am6/E
(JOS)
Em
Am6/E
Bsus4/E
B/E
Ro- man ar- mies in their le- gions,
see them march from town to town.
Ah-
Am6/E
(MARY)
Em
Am6/E
Bsus4/E
B/E
They are sol- diers to look up to,
but our God is loo- king down!
Fm7
(M & J)
Bsus4/B
B
Em
God is loo- king!
Sure- ly He has got a frown!
Sure- ly He has got a frown!

Em
D
Em
God in hea- ven rules!
Lit- tle men are fools!
(JOS)
(MARY) God in hea- ven rules!
Lit- tle men are
D
Em
God in hea- ven rules!
Lit- tle men are fools!
fools!
God in hea- ven rules!
Lit- tle men are
Am6/E
Em
Am6/E
Bsus4/E
B/E
(JOS)
Ro- man ar- mies in their le- gions,
see them march from town to town.
(choir)
Ah -
fools!

Am6/E
(MARY)
Em
Am6/E
Bsus4/E
B/E
They are sol- diers to look up to, but our God is loo- king down!
Ah-
Fm7
(M & J)
Bsus4/B
B
Em
Fm7
God is loo- king! Sure- ly He has got a frown! God is loo- king!
Sure- ly He has got a frown!
Bsus4/B
B
Em
Sure- ly He has got a frown! Mo- ney! Mo- ney! Mo- ney!
Sure- ly He has got a frown!
(shout)
He wants more!

SIMEON *The Roman Census meant that Joseph, who could trace his family tree back to King David, must take Mary and make the long tiring journey into the hill-country of Judea, to what was known as "David's town" - the little village of Bethlehem.*

(4) MARY AND HER MAN

Martin Parry **Roger Jones**

Am7 Dm G/D Dm C/D
Beth-le- hem.
came to him.
(TB) Ma- ry's ba- by due so soon, Jo- seph asks them "Is there room?"
(SOLO) I've a sta-ble, pret-ty dry, nice and warm, give it a try -
Dm G/D B♭maj7 Am7
"Sor- ry" they all say to him, "There is no room in Beth- le-
all I have, not much I fear, but all you're going to find 'round
Dm G/D Dm G/D Dm G/D
Go- ing down, go- ing down, go- ing down to
hem.
here."
(TB) Go- ing down, go- ing down to

B♭maj7
Am7
Dm
G/D
Dm
G/D
Beth- le- hem town. Go- ing down, go- ing down,
Beth- le- hem town. Go- ing down, go- ing
Dm
G/D
B♭maj7
Am7
Dm
G/D
go- ing down to Beth- le- hem town.
down to Beth- le- hem town.
Dm
G/D
Dm
G/D
Dm
G/D

Em
A/E
Em
D/E
(SA) So at last her Boy was born, Ma- ry's child in Beth- le- hem,
Em
A/E
Cmaj7
Bm7
in that sta- ble of the inn, Ma- ry's child of Beth- le-
(TB)
Em
A/E
Em
D/E
hem.
In the heav'ns the an- gels sang, hal- le- lu- jahs rang and rang:

Em
A/E
Cmaj7
Bm7
Peace on earth, good-will to men, through the child of Beth-le-
Em
A/E
Em
A/E
Em
A/E
Cmaj7
(SA) Sing to Him, sing to Him, to the Child of Beth-le-
hem. Sing to Him, to the Child of Beth-le-
Bm7
Em
A/E
Em
A/E
Em
A/E
hem. Sing to Him, sing to Him, to the Child of
hem. Sing to Him, to the Child of

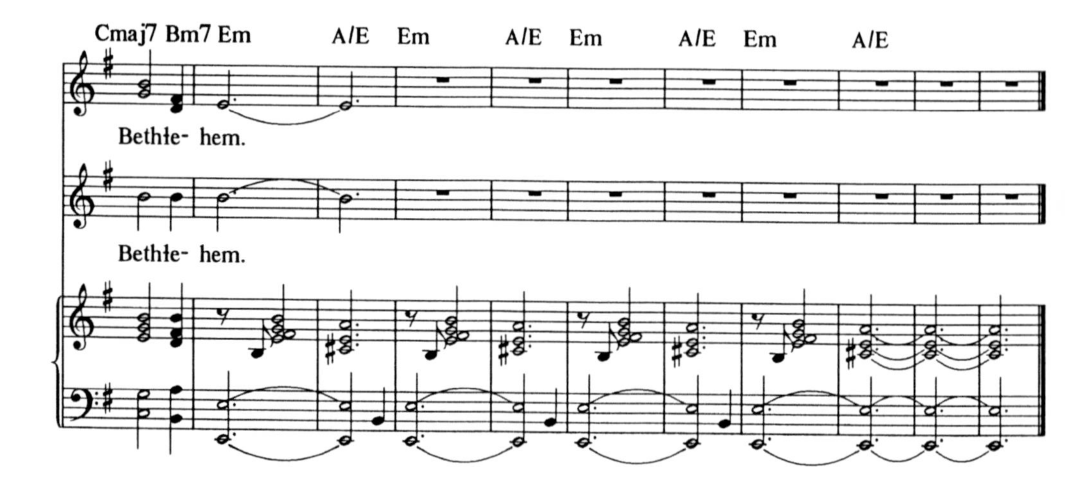

SIMEON *So there, in the humble surroundings of the Bethlehem stable, Mary wrapped her son in strips of cloth, and laid him in a manger. Meanwhile, in the fields outside the town, a group of shepherds were huddled around their camp-fire for warmth, watching their flock of sheep, scattered around the hill-side. Suddenly there was a bright light, and an angel appeared to them. They were terrified. "Don't be afraid!", said the angel. "I'm bringing you Good News - wonderful news, of great joy, to everyone on earth! Today, in 'David's town', a Saviour has been born for you - the Messiah - the Anointed One!" And all at once the sky seemed to be overflowing with angels, singing together and praising God.*

(5) GLORY TO GOD

Glory to God in the highest **Roger Jones**

G
C/G
F
D
Peace to His peo- ple, peace to His peo- ple on earth!
G
C/G
G
C/G
Glo- ry to God! Glo- ry to God in the high- est!
G
C/G
G C/G G
Peace to His peo- ple, peace to His peo- ple on earth!
(SA)
C
G
D
Am7/G G
Lord God, hea- ven- ly King, al-migh- ty God and Fa- ther,

(SATB)
C
G
F
to You our praises we bring, you are God!
D
C (SA)
G
D
Lord God, heavenly King, almighty God and
Am7/G G
(SATB)
C
G
F
C/E
Father, to You our praises we bring, you are God!

F
C/E
D
C/D
D
you are God!
Chorus
G
(descant)
C/G
G
Glo- ry to God!
Glo- ry to God!
(choir)
Glo- ry to God!
Glo- ry to God in the high- est!
C/G
G
C/G
Peace to His peo- le, peo- ple on
Peace to His peo- ple, peace to His peo- ple on

F
D
G
earth!
Glo- ry to God!
earth!
Glo- ry to God!
C/G
G
C/G
Glo- ry to God!
Glo- ry to God in the high- est!
G
C/G
G
C/G G
Peace to His peo- ple, peo- ple on earth!
2nd time to CODA
Peace to His peo- ple, peace to His peo- ple on earth!

F
G
F
G
(SA) Lord Je- sus Christ, on- ly Son of the Fa- ther,
F
C/E
Gsus4
G
F
Lord God, Lamb of God; (SATB) You've come to
G
F
G
F
take a- way the sin of the world: have mer- cy on us,
Dsus4
D
have mer- cy on us!
1st time back to

CODA
C
G
D
You a- lone are the Ho- ly One, You a- lone
G
C
G
F
are the Lord, You a- lone are the Most High God,
D
C
G
D
Je- sus Christ, with the Ho- ly

G
C
G
Spi- rit, in the glo- ry of God the
F
C
D
E♭
Fa- ther, the Fa- ther!
A♭
(descant)
D♭/Ab
A♭
Glo- ry to God!
Glo- ry to God!
(choir)
Glo- ry to God!
Glo- ry to God in the high- est!

D♭/Ab
A♭
D♭/Ab
Peace to His peo- ple, peo- ple on
Peace to His peo- ple, peace to His peo- ple on
G♭
E♭7
A♭
earth! Glo- ry to God!
earth! Glo- ry to God!
D♭/Ab
A♭
D♭/Ab
Glo- ry to God!
Glo- ry to God in the high- est!

SIMEON *The angel had told the shepherds that they would find the baby in Bethlehem lying in a manger and wrapped in strips of cloth. Once they had got over the shock of what they had just seen and heard, they wasted no time in doing as he had said.*

(6) LET US GO TO BE

Em
Am7
B7
3
Em
F#m7 Em
So we'll go there just as we were bid- den.
G
(SOLO)
D/F#
Em
Bm/D
"Do you think" said the first "He'll be hand- some bright?"
"Do you think" said the third wai- ting to be heard,
C
D/C
G/B
D/A
G
"Oh of course" said the se- cond "that just must be right!"
"that he'll wear blue and gol- den cloth, draped fold by fold?"
G
D/F#
Em
Bm/D
Will He look quite grand, hol- ding out His hands, and
"Yes" then said the fourth as they hea- ded north. "And

Fmaj7
1 Bsus4 B7
2 Bsus4 B7
p'raps just floa- ting off the ground!"
now then, what do you think, lad?" (choir) The
F slower D G E♭ F E♭
last in their clan was- n't quite yet a man, he was qui- et and thought- ful,
Bsus4 B7 (SOLO) F D G E♭
kind. "What I think you may ask, well, you've set me a task when I
F E♭ Bsus4 C7
think Who we soon might find!

1st time: Instruments only
Fm
B♭m7
C7
Fm
Gm7
C7
(choir) We have come to be in the com- pa- ny
Fm
B♭m7
C7
3
Fm
Gm7
Fm
of the one who brings an- gels from hea- ven.
Fm
B♭m7
C7
Fm
Gm7
C7
Can this real- ly be Him in ma- jes- ty?
Fm
B♭m7
C7
3
Fm
Gm7
Fm
But we've come here just as we were bid- den.

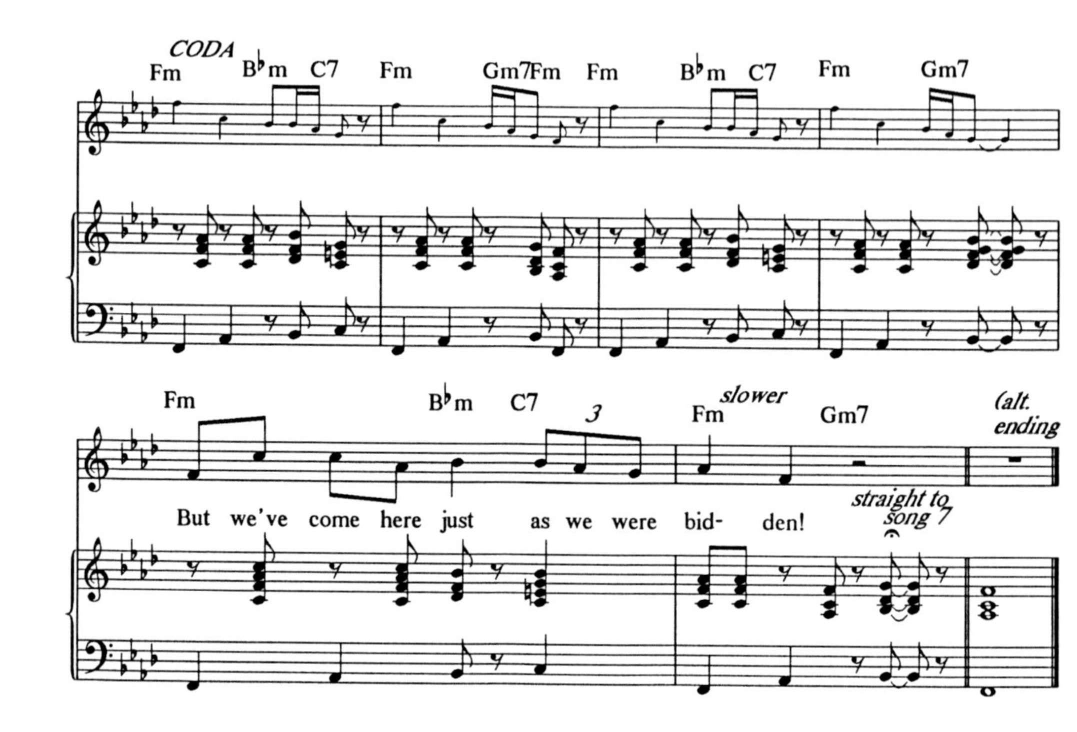

SIMEON *In the Bethlehem stable, they found Mary and Joseph, and the baby lying in the manger, just as the angel had said, and then and there they knelt down and worshipped the Christ-child*

(7) O LITTLE TOWN OF BETHLEHEM

P. Brooks (1835-93)

Roger Jones

F Gm7/F F Gm7/F F Gm7/F
thee lie! A- bove thy deep and dream- less sleep
F Gm7/F F Gm7/F F Gm7/F F
The si- lent stars go by.
B♭ C/Bb Am7 F7
Yet in the dark streets shi- neth
B♭ C F Gm7 F Gm7 A7
The e- ver- las- ting light; The hopes and fears of

Dm
Dm7
B♭maj7
Gm7
Csus4
C7
all the years are met in thee to- night.
F
Gm7/F
Am/F
GM7
F
Gm7/F
Am/F
GM7
F
Gm7/F
F
Gm7/F
(MARY) O mor- ning
(JOS) O mor- ning stars, to- geth- er pro- claim the ho-
F
Gm7/F
F
Gm7/F
stars pro- claim the ho- ly birth,
ly birth,

F Gm7/F F Gm7/F
and prai- ses
and prai- ses sing to God the King, and peace to men
F Gm7/F F Gm7/F F
sing, and peace to men on earth;
on earth;
B♭ C/Bb Am F7
for Christ is born of
for Christ is born of Ma- ry,

B♭ C F Gm7 F Gm7 A7
Ma - ry!
and ga- thered all a-bove, while mor- tals sleep, the
Dm Dm7 B♭maj7 Gm7 Csus4
While an- gels watch in won-d'ring love!
an-gels keep their watch of won- d'ring love.
F Gm7/F F Gm7/F
(SATB) How si- lent- ly, how si- lent- ly, the won- drous gift

F
Gm7/F
F
Gm7/F
F
Gm7/F
is given!
So God im- parts to hu- man hearts
F
Gm7/F
F
Gm7/F
F
Gm7/F
the bles- sing of His heaven.
B♭
C7/Bb
Am
F7
B♭
C7
No ear may hear His co- ming;
but in this world of

F
B♭
Asus4
A7
Dm
sin, where meek souls will re- ceive Him, still the dear Christ
B♭maj7
Gm7
Csus4
C7
F
B♭/F
F
C/D
D7
en- ters in.
G
C
G
C
G
C
(JOS) O ho- ly Child, de-scend to us
(choir) O ho-ly Child of Beth-le-hem, de-scend to us, we pray;

G C G C G C
we pray;
cast out our
cast out our sin, and en- ter in;
be born in us
G C G Am7 G/B
sin, be born in us to- day!
to- day.
C D7 Bm G7
We hear the Christ- mas
We hear the Christ- mas an- gels

C D G Am7 G Am7 Bsus4 B7
an - gels!
the great glad ti- dings tell;
O come to us, a-
Em Cmaj7 Am7 Dsus4 D7
O come, our Lord, Im- ma- nu- el!
bide with us, our Lord Im- ma- nu- el!
G Am7/G Gmaj7 Am7/G
O ho- ly Child of Beth- le- hem,
(choir) Our Lord Im- man- u-

G (MARY)
Am7/G
Gmaj7
Am7/G
cast out our sin, and en- ter in;
el!
Our Lord Im- man- u-
G (JOS)
Am7/G
Gmaj7
Am7/G
O come to us, a- bide with us,
el!
Our Lord Im- man- u-
G (M & J)
Am7/G
Gmaj7
Am7/G
G
Am7/G
O come to us, a- bide with us,
el!
Our Lord Im-man- u- el!
ad lib .....
Gmaj7
Am7/G
G
Am7/G
G
Am7/G
G

SIMEON *All that took place just a week ago. And now, here I stand in the Temple courtyard, with that same baby in my arms, and these old eyes of mine fill with tears of gratitude and praise, for I know that they have indeed seen 'The Salvation of Israel'.*

(8) LORD, NOW LET YOUR SERVANT

Nunc Dimittis

Roger Jones

(SIM)
Dm
Gm9 Am7 Dm
Dm
C
Nunc di-mit- tis
Lord we pray!
Lord, now let your ser- vant de-
Lord we pray!
(choir)
B♭
Am7
Gm7
Am7
Dm
C/D
part in peace, ac-cor-ding
to your
word.
(SIM)
Dm
C
B♭
Am7
(choir)
Gm7
Am7
Lord, now let your ser- vant de-
part in peace, ac-cor-ding
to your

Dm
Gm7
(SIM)
C7
Fsus2
Dm7
word.
For my eyes have
seen,
they have
Gm7
Asus4
Dm
Gm7
Csus4
C7
seen
your sal-
va-
tion,
which you have pre-
Fsus2
Dm7
Gm7
Gm/Bb
Asus4
A
pared
be-
fore the
face
of all
peo- ple.

(choir)
Gm7
C7
F7
Dm7
To be a light to ligh- ten the gen- tiles,
Gm7
C7
F
to be the glo- ry of Your peo- ple Is- ra- el.
Gm7
C
F
Dm7
To be a light to ligh- ten the gen- tiles, and

Gm7
Gm7/E
Asus/4
Gdim7/A
Dm
glo- ry to Is- ra- el!
Nunc di-mit- tis
C
Dm
Gm9 Am7 Dm
Nunc di-mit- tis
Lord we pray!
Nunc di-mit- tis
Lord we pray!
Dm
C
Dm
Nunc di-mit- tis
Nunc di-mit- tis
Nunc di-mit- tis

(SIM)
(choir)
Gm9Am7Dm
Dm
C
B♭
Am7
Lord we pray!
Lord, now let your ser- vant de- part in peace, ac-cor-ding
(1st - Instruments only, 2nd - Voices)
Lord we pray!
Gm7
Am7
Dm
C/D
Dm
C
to your word.
Lord, now let your ser- vant de-
B♭
Am7
Gm7
Am7
Dm
part in peace, ac-cor- ding to your word.

SIMEON *I see the prophetess Anna approaching us - a lovely, Spirit-filled lady. She never leaves the temple precincts, day or night, but is always worshipping God in fasting and in prayer. Like me, she too has been longing and waiting for this moment for many years.*

(9) I WAITED PATIENTLY FOR THE LORD

Anna's Song - From Psalm 40

Roger Jones

A7
3
Dm
He turned His ear and lis- tened to me.
Vocal both times
Gm
Dm
Out of the sli- my pit, out of the mud and mire -
Gm
A7
Dm
He set me on a rock, He made me stand up high- er!
Gm
Dm
A new song in my mouth of praise un- to our God;

2nd time to CODA
E♭
Asus4
A
ma- ny now will see and fear and put their trust in the Lord!
A7
Dm
A7
Wait for the Lord!
Wait for the Lord!
Wait for the Lord!
Wait for the Lord!
Dm
A7
Dm
Wait for the Lord!
Wait for the Lord!
Wait for the Lord!
Wait for the Lord!
Wait for the Lord!
Wait for the Lord!

A7
3
Dm
For now the Lord has come - to me!
CODA
A7
Dm
A7
Wait for the Lord!
Wait for the Lord!
Wait for the Lord!
Wait for the Lord!
Dm
A7
3
Wait for the Lord!
I wai- ted pa- tient- ly for the Lord,
Wait for the Lord!
Wait for the Lord!

Dm
A7
3
He turned His ear and lis- tened to
Wait for the Lord!
Wait for the Lord!
Dm
A7
3
me.
I wai- ted pa- tient- ly for the Lord,
Wait for the Lord!
Wait for the Lord!

SIMEON *How wonderful that in my old age, I have seen God in this child - that same God who spoke through His angel messenger to Mary and the same God who spoke through His heavenly host to the shepherds! Why should I be so favoured, that my Lord should visit me?*

(10) FINALE

- Why should I be so favoured? - Nunc dimittis - Glory

Roger Jones

B♭
E♭/Bb
Fsus4
Cm/F
F7
(MARY) I will mag-ni-fy the Lord!
(choir) I will mag-ni-fy the Lord!
B♭
E♭/Bb
Fsus4
Cm/F
F7
I will mag-ni-fy the Lord!
I will mag-ni-fy the Lord!
Oh -
B♭
E♭/Bb
Fsus4
I will
I will mag- ni- fy the Lord!

D9/F#
Gm7
mag- ni- fy the Lord!
Praise His name, proc- laim His word,
Cm/Eb
E♭sus2
B♭
B♭sus4
Asus4
A
He is my God!
slow down
more relaxed
♩ = 80
Dm
C
(SA) Nunc di- mit- tis
(TB) Nunc di- mit- tis

Dm
Gm9 Am7 Dm
Dm
Nunc di- mit- tis
Lord we pray!
Nunc di- mit- tis
Lord we pray!
C
Dm
Gm9 Am7 Dm
Nunc di- mit- tis
Lord we pray!
Nunc di- mit- tis
Lord we pray!
= 150
G
C/G
G
(descant) Glo- ry to God!
Glo- ry to God!
(choir) Glo- ry to God!
Glo- ry to God in the high- est!

C/G
G
C/G
Peace to His peo- ple, peo- ple on
Peace to His peo- ple, peace to His peo- ple on
F
D7
G
earth!
Glo- ry to God!
earth!
Glo- ry to God!
C/G
G
C/G
Glo- ry to God!
Glo- ry to God in the high- est!

G
C/G
G
C/G
G
Peace to His peo- ple, peo- ple on earth!
Peace to His peo- ple, peace to His peo- ple on earth!
CODA
G
G/C
G
(Descant) Glo- ry to God!
Glo- ry to God!
(SA) Glo- ry to God!
Glo- ry to God!
(TB) Glo- ry to God!
G/C
G
Glo- ry to God!
Glo- ry to God!
Glo- ry to God!

G/C
G
Glo- ry to God!
Glo- ry to God!
Glo- ry to God!

Simeon

VOCAL SCORE
WORDS ONLY
CD
CASSETTE
ACCOMPANIMENT CD
DRAMA
INSTRUMENTAL PARTS